Man Eater

by

S. P. Gates

Illustrated by Dylan Gibson

With special thanks to:

Anne Bergin
Amelia Brown
Frances Burrage
Aaron Cam
Lorenzo Cimmino
Jade Claybroor
Katie Conneely
Charlie David
Lucy Davis
Nick Goldsborough
Sophie Hall
Tom Ing
Louise Isaacs
Katherine Keeble
Aaron Keeley
Jordon Moore
Rachel Nalletamby
Louis Philpot
Daniel Stone
Bailey Turner
Shane Walker
Tom Wiltshire
Bradley Yendall
Max Yendall

First published in 2010 in Great Britain by
Barrington Stoke Ltd
18 Walker St, Edinburgh, EH3 7LP

www.barringtonstoke.co.uk

Copyright © 2010 S. P. Gates
Illustrations © Dylan Gibson

The moral right of the author has been asserted in accordance with the Copyright, Designs and Patents Act 1988

ISBN: 978-1-84299-826-7

Printed in Great Britain by Bell & Bain Ltd

Contents

GROCERY
Repairing
RADIOS
&
BATTERY
CHARGE

Levi is 13 years old. He lives in a village in East Africa. Now read one of his adventures!

Chapter 1
Gran's Scary Stories

Levi was walking past Gran's house. She was sitting outside, sipping a beer. She was telling spooky stories to David, Levi's little brother.

"Do you know the pond up that hill?" Gran asked David. She pointed to a hill above the village.

“Yes,” said David.

“A huge snake lives in that pond,” said Gran. “He’s a monster! He can squeeze a cow to death.”

Levi laughed. He said, “Gran, there isn’t any monster snake up there. Stop spooking David with your crazy stories.”

David didn't think Gran's story was crazy. But he wasn't spooked at all. He said, "Wow! I'd like to see that monster snake!"

Later, Levi told his mum, "I'm going to play football with my mates."

"OK, but I have to go to the market," said Levi's mum. "Will you look after David?"

“Do I have to?” groaned Levi. “He’s just a baby. He’ll get in my way.”

Levi’s mum began to get mad. “You lazy boy!” she told Levi. “You never help out! You never look after David. And I work my fingers to the bone!”

Levi groaned again. He could see a big row coming.

“All right, Mum.” He nodded. “I’ll look after David. As long as it’s not for long.”

Chapter 2
“Mum’s Going to Kill Me!”

Levi walked to the football field with David.

He told David to sit down under a tree. “Stay here,” Levi said. “Watch the game. And don’t get in the way.”

Levi started to play football with his mates. He forgot about David – all he could think about was the game.

It was a great game. Levi scored two goals and his team won, 3 : 2.

When the game ended, his mates crowded round. "Hey, man, you played well today," they said, slapping him on the back.

Then suddenly Levi remembered about David. He looked under the tree. But his little brother wasn't there.

At first Levi wasn't too worried. David might have got bored and toddled off somewhere.

"I bet he's gone to see Gran," Levi told himself.

Levi went running to Gran's house. She was weeding her sweet corn.

"Have you seen David?" he asked her.

"No," Gran told him. "He hasn't been here. Mum said you were looking after him."

Levi went running around the village. He asked everyone he met, “Have you seen my little brother?”

But everyone shook their heads. No one had seen David anywhere.

Now Levi was starting to panic. *Mum's going to kill me!* he said to himself. *I'd better find David quick, before she gets back from the market.*

Chapter 3
"Don't Shoot!"

Then at last a little girl told Levi, "Yes, I've seen David."

"Where?" said Levi. "Tell me quick!"

"He went up there," said the girl.

The girl pointed up the hill, behind the village. “He said he was going to see the monster snake.”

“Oh, no!” said Levi. He was frantic now.

“I don’t believe in any old monster snake,” said the little girl, as she skipped away. “That’s just silly!”

Levi didn't think there was really a monster snake up there either. But the hill was full of danger for little boys. It was thick with trees and bushes. Wild animals lived up there. What if David got lost? What if a wild animal found him?

Levi went racing up the hill, to the pond. He was really in a panic now. He crashed through the trees and bushes. He tripped over a rock and fell down. Blood poured from his knees and ran down his legs. But Levi picked himself up and went on running.

Suddenly Levi heard a noise in the bushes. He stopped and looked around.

“Who’s there?” he said. “David, is that you?”

A soldier jumped out of the bushes, right in front of Levi. Levi could see he had a gun.

“Don’t shoot!” said Levi, putting his hands up.

Chapter 4
"That Lion is a Killer!"

But the soldier had put his gun away.

He took off his cap so that Levi could see his face.

"James, it's you!" Levi said, amazed.

He put his hands down again.

James was a friend from his village. He'd left home last year to join the army.

"It's good to see you again, James!" said Levi. "But what are you soldiers doing here?"

"We are hunting a lion," said James. "We think it's up near the pond."

“But my brother David’s up there!” said Levi. “I’m going to find him.”

James looked grim. “This lion is a killer,” said James. “It attacked a man in the next village. It’s a man eater.”

“Come on!” yelled Levi. “Help me look. We’ve got to find David before the lion does.”

The two boys rushed up the hill.

Levi tried to keep calm. But he couldn’t. What if the lion had already found David?

Levi thought, *Why didn't I take better care of my brother? If anything bad happens to him, I'll be to blame. I shall feel awful for the rest of my life.*

To take his mind off his fears, he started talking to James.

"What's it like in the army?" he asked him, as they ran up the hill.

Levi thought his friend looked hungry. He thought James's uniform looked scruffy. It was too big for him.

But James said, “The army is great! They treat us like kings. They gave me my gun.”

“Show me it!” begged Levi. “I want to see it!”

But James didn’t show Levi his gun. He just told him, “It’s the best gun in the world! And I’m a crack shot!”

“Will you shoot the lion if you see him?” asked Levi.

“Of course,” said James. “With one shot! Right between the eyes!”

Chapter 5
Lion Attack

Levi's heart gave a leap of joy. "There's David!" he yelled to James. "We've found him. He's safe!"

David was sitting by the pond.

Levi shouted, "It's all right, David, we're here."

But David didn't even look at Levi. He was watching something in the long grass. "Lion!" he shouted.

Levi looked to where David was pointing. All he could see were two golden eyes. Levi's heart almost stopped.

"The lion's in the long grass over there," he said softly to James. "It's seen David. Shoot it. Shoot it right now."

But James did nothing.

"Why are you waiting?" asked Levi.

The grass shook. The golden eyes moved closer.

"It's going to kill David! Use your gun!" Levi begged James. "Shoot it!"

In a tiny voice, James said, "I can't shoot it."

“What are you talking about?” yelled Levi. “You’ve got a gun, haven’t you?”

James drew his gun.

He showed it to Levi. “It’s not a real gun,” he said. “It’s only made of wood. It’s useless!”

Suddenly the grass shook again. The lion growled. Its eyes were like two golden fires.

“The lion’s going to attack!” said Levi.

Both boys started yelling as loud as they could. They threw sticks and rocks, anything they could find, trying to scare the lion away.

But the lion wasn't scared. It came creeping out of the long grass. Its eyes were fixed on David. It growled again. Then it crouched, ready to spring.

Chapter 6
Monster Snake

But, suddenly, the lion stopped. It wasn't staring at David any more. It had seen something else. A huge snake was swimming across the pond.

"It's a python!" said Levi, amazed. It was the biggest python he'd ever seen.

So Gran's story was true, after all.

"David," said Levi, "keep very still."

The python slid out of the water and over the rocks. Its forked tongue flicked in and out of its mouth. But it wasn't after David. It slid towards the lion.

With a roar, the lion jumped at the python and dug its claws into its scaly skin. But, quick as a flash, the snake twisted itself around the lion's body. The lion roared again and tried to bite it.

But the python began to squeeze. It squeezed and squeezed until the lion crashed onto the ground. The lion stopped growling. Its body twitched. Then, at last, it lay still.

The python let go of the lion.

While Levi and James watched in horror, the python tried to eat the lion. The snake opened its jaws wide. It fitted them around the lion's head. It half swallowed the head. But the rest wouldn't go down. So the snake opened its mouth really wide. Its jaws almost ripped apart! But it was no good. The lion's head was just too big to swallow. The snake had to spit the lion out. It slid away, hissing, looking for something smaller to eat.

Then it picked up David's smell.

It slid towards him.

"Throw a rock at it!" yelled Levi.

But there were no rocks left to throw. They'd thrown them all at the lion. So James threw his wooden gun instead. It hit the python on the head and scared it away. The python slid back into the pond and swam away.

Chapter 7
Poor Old Lion

Levi and James couldn't believe what they had just seen.

"Is that lion really dead?" asked James.

"It's not moving," said Levi.

Levi ran to get David. First, he gave him a big hug.

"You're safe!" he told David. "You're safe now!"

But David didn't seem to know that his life had been in danger.

"I saw the monster snake!" he told Levi. "Just like Grandma said!"

Levi went over to the lion. He crept up with great care. He took a long look. The lion's eyes were closed. Levi poked it with a stick. Then he shouted to James, "It's OK, it's dead."

James came over.

"I didn't think a python could kill a lion," Levi said.

“It was a very big python,” said James. “And this is an old sick lion. Look at it. It’s hardly got any teeth left. And it’s so skinny. It’s a bag of bones.”

“That’s why it became a man eater,” said Levi, “because it was too sick to chase deer or zebra.”

"Poor old lion," said James, looking down at its body. "It must have been starving."

"I don't feel sorry for it," Levi said. "It nearly ate my brother."

James looked around. "We'd better get out of here," he told Levi, "before that python comes back."

Chapter 8

"Goodbye, James! Good Luck!"

Levi carried David down the hill. David fell asleep on Levi's back. He was worn out, after all his adventures.

Levi asked James, "Why was your gun only made of wood?"

James said, "I was lying about the army. The truth is, I hate it! Look at this stupid uniform. It's ragged and too big. And they don't give us much to eat. I'm always hungry! And I haven't been paid any wages. And they don't have real guns for us boys. We just get wooden ones."

"So are you going back?" asked Levi.

"No," said James. "I'm sick of the army. I'm never going back."

"Why don't you come home to the village?" said Levi. "We could have some good fun. We could play football, just like we used to do."

But James said, "No, I can't. How can I face my parents? I have written them letters. I've told them that I love the army and that I am doing great!"

Levi said, "I'm sure they'll understand when you tell them what it's really like."

"The truth is I can't live in our village any more," said James. It's too boring for me. I'm off to the big city!"

"What are you going to do in the city?" asked Levi.

"I'm going to look for a job. I'm going to make lots of money and be a big man!"

They got to the main road, that led to the city.

James said, "This is where I say goodbye."

The two friends shook hands. Levi didn't know what to say, so he just said, "See you, man."

Sadly he watched James walk away down the long, dusty road. James looked lonely, but brave.

"Goodbye, James," Levi suddenly called after his friend. "Good luck!"

James turned round and waved. Then he walked on, down the road, to the city.

Have you read Levi's first adventure?

Killer Croc

Levi is in danger. There's a killer croc on the loose – and it's hungry! Can he escape its jaws?

For more info visit our website at
www.barringtonstoke.co.uk

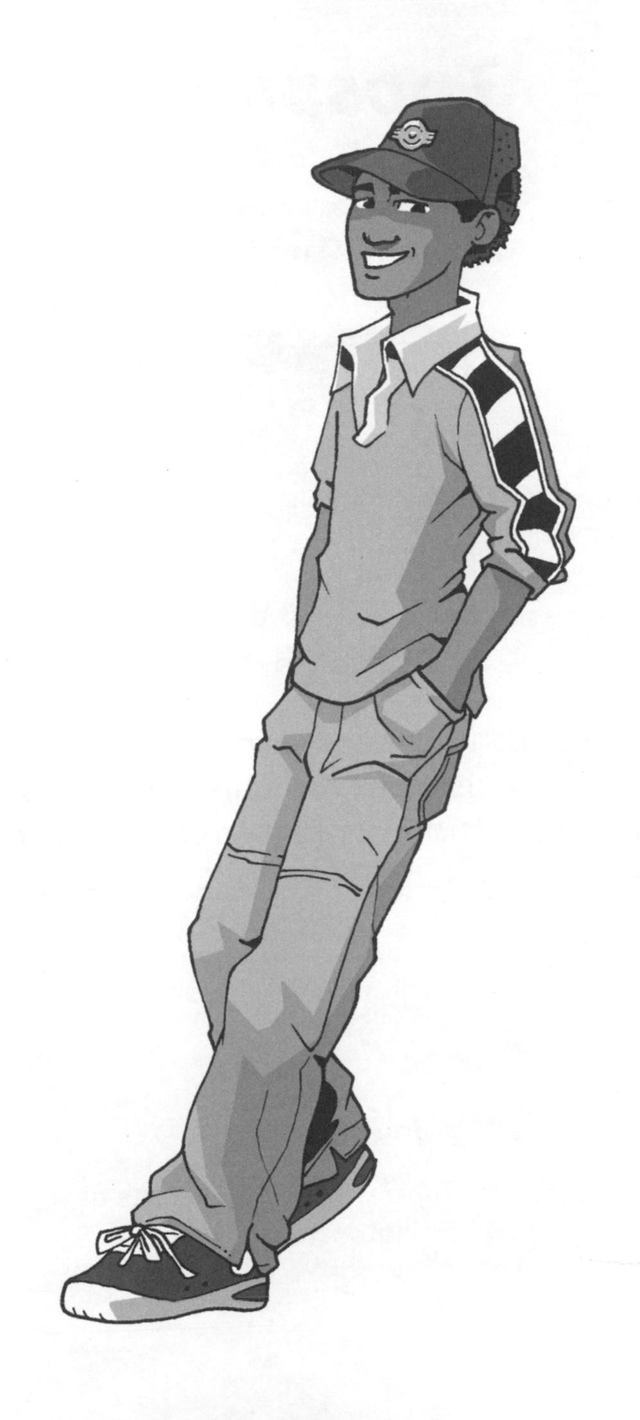

Topspin

by
Sean Callery

Tim needs to learn the topspin serve to win the tennis final. But his dad is his tennis coach, and he's just walked out on the family. Can Tim do it alone?

You can order *Topspin* from our website at www.barringtonstoke.co.uk

Extreme Race

by

Jane A. C. West

Mark and Ben plan to run 150 miles, across the Sahara desert, to raise money for Ben's sick sister. Will they survive sandstorms, sunburn, freezing nights and 40°C days – and finish the race?

You can order *Extreme Race* from our website at www.barringtonstoke.co.uk

Lucky

by

S. P. Gates

Everyone thinks because Dom is big, he's a bully. But Leon knows what he's really like. And when an injured seagull needs their help, Leon finds out there's more to Dom than he thought.

You can order *Lucky* from our website at www.barringtonstoke.co.uk